JOSEPH HAYDN

QUARTET

for 2 Violins, Viola and Violoncello
E♭ major/Es-Dur/Mi♭ majeur
Hob. III: 38
(Opus 33/2)

Edited by/Herausgegeben von
Wilhelm Altmann

Ernst Eulenburg Ltd
London · Mainz · Madrid · New York · Paris · Tokyo · Toronto · Zürich

All rights reserved. No part of this publication may be reproduced, stored in a retrieval system, or transmitted in any form or by any means, electronic, mechanical, photocopying, recording or otherwise, without the prior written permission of Ernst Eulenburg Ltd., 48 Great Marlborough Street, London W1V 2BN.

Quartet No. 38

I

Joseph Haydn, Op. 33, No. 2
1732-1809

E.E. 1152

Ernst Eulenburg Ltd

20
cresc.
cresc.
cresc.
cresc.
f
f
f
f
p
p
p
p
f
f
f
f
6
6
mezza
mezza
voce
voce
mezza voce
30
p
p
p
p

p
f
p
f
p
f
p
f
40
p
p
sf
sf
sf
p
sf

50
p
cresc.
mf
f
60

70

80
cresc.
cresc.
cresc.
cresc.
f
f
f
f
p
p
p
p
f
f
f
f
tr
mezzo voce
mezzo voce
mezzo voce
p
p
p
p
90

II

30
Fine
Trio
40
50

60
Scherzo D.C. al Fine
III
Largo sostenuto
dolce
p
10
dolce
p
pp

tr
f
ff
p
20
f sf sf sf
pp
30
dim.
sf
pp

40
f sf sf sf
f pp p
mf
p
sf sf
50
dolce

tr
60
p
f
mf
cresc.
3
70
pp

IV

60
sf
stacc.
stacc.
stacc.
70
p
80

mf
90
p
p
cresc.
cresc.
cresc.
cresc.
100
p
p
p
p
110
f
f
f
f
f

120
staccato
stacc. sempre
130
140
f
p
pp

Adagio
150
Presto
1
G.P.
160
3
170
Fine